CO TYRONE

Edited by Lynsey Hawkins

First published in Great Britain in 2003 by
YOUNG WRITERS
Remus House,
Coltsfoot Drive,
Peterborough, PE2 9JX
Telephone (01733) 890066

HB ISBN 1 84460 036 X
SB ISBN 1 84460 037 8

FOREWORD

Young Writers was established in 1991 as a foundation for promoting the reading and writing of poetry amongst children and young adults. Today it continues this quest and proceeds to nurture and guide the writing talents of today's youth.

From this year's competition Young Writers is proud to present a showcase of the best poetic talent from across the UK. Each hand-picked poem has been carefully chosen from over 66,000 'Hullabaloo!' entries to be published in this, our eleventh primary school series.

This year in particular we have been wholeheartedly impressed with the quality of entries received. The thought, effort, imagination and hard work put into each poem impressed us all and once again the task of editing was a difficult but enjoyable experience.

We hope you are as pleased as we are with the final selection and that you and your family will continue to be entertained with *Hullabaloo! Co Tyrone* for many years to come.

CONTENTS

Evish Primary School

St Mary's Primary School, Stewartstown

Barry Quinn	69
Una McCann	70
Hannah Devlin	71
Christopher Coyle	72
Nicola Coyle	72
Caoimhe Mulgrew	73
Naomi Robinson	73
Christopher McNally	74
Laura Tierney	74

St Patrick's Primary School, Castlederg

Natalie McKay	75
Seanain McGuigan	76
Maureen Bogle	77
Colette Corry	77
Edel Byrne	78
Conaill Carolan	79
Patrick McAnea	80
Niall Lynch	82
Grainne McGirr	82

St Patrick's Primary School, Dungannon

Emma Clements	83
Shannon Lafferty	84
Kelly Mallon	84
Lauren Watson	85
Catherine Winters	85
Sorcha Dinsmore	86
James Murphy	86
Rebecca Hand	87
Conor McNeill	87
Marianne McCann	88
Rory McCooey	88
Sarah Loughran	89
Rebecca McGuigan	89
Rachel Kane	90
Oisin Shields	90

Sean Hughes	91
Kyna Dinsmore	91
Andrew Murphy	92
Sarah Canavan	92
Daniel Maguire	93
Dermott Burns	93
Gareth Cullen	94
Arthur Rafferty	94
David Mills	95
Conor McNally	95
Niall Kelly	96
Laury Deery	96
Eimear Casey	97
Meghan McCaul	97
Anna Deery	98
Shae McKernan	98
Cara Donnelly	99
Naomi Campbell	100
Andrew Watson	100
Aimee-Lee Kinnear	100
Marian Barker	101
David McManus	101
Gerard Currie	102
Ryan Devlin	102
Lorchan Ritchie	103
Helen Kerr	103
Kerrie-Ann Kelly	104

St Peter's Primary School, Plumbridge

Catherine Morris	104
Seamus Maloney	105
Christina McAneney	105
Ciara Furey	106
Joseph Murray	106
Philip McBride	107
Ciaran McNulty	107
Amanda Hood	108
Leon McNamee	108

The Poems

The Wonderful Weather

W indy breeze like a tornado,
E xtremely hot is the sun,
A ir like a table, it's so thick,
T eeming rain flowing from nowhere,
H ailstones like massive golf balls hit your head,
E verywhere you go you see some kind of weather,
R arely the way we want it!

Victoria Riddles (10)
Artigarvan Primary School

Football

Football used to be boring,
But now Michael Owen is scoring,
He scores with his head
And he scores with his foot,
He's won the golden boot.

David Riddles (10)
Artigarvan Primary School

Dog

I have a collie sheepdog,
It likes to jump over logs,
It caught a mouse,
Brought it into the house!
It made my mum scream
And that was the last it was ever seen!

Jill McKean (10)
Artigarvan Primary School

SCAMP

One day my mum
Brought a pup home,
She put it in my arms,
It was so soft and warm.
I asked her why she brought it home,
She said it was all left alone.
My mum asked, 'What's its name?'
I shouted, 'Scamp!'
And my brother said the same.

Victoria Temple (11)
Artigarvan Primary School

BROTHERS

They're just an accident waiting to happen,
Always messing around with you,
Never getting anywhere,
You tell them, 'Get a life!'
You tell them, 'Go away!'
But na aw! No way!

Julie Mills (10)
Artigarvan Primary School

DOLPHINS

I like dolphins,
I like their fins,
They swim, they splash,
They don't even crash,
They eat squid and fish,
(Not out of a dish!)

Dolphins live in groups,
Some do tricks through hoops,
They communicate through clicks,
As fast as the clock ticks,
Dolphins are the best in the world!

Natasha Dinsmore (11)
Artigarvan Primary School

SCRAMBLER

S   is for safety, always wear a helmet.
C   is for children who are having fun.
R   is for race track.
A   is for adult supervision.
M   is for motorbikes to ride on.
B   is for boots and body armour.
L   is for liking this sport.
E   is for excitement when you win a race.
R   is for ramps to jump over.

Steven Finlay (11)
Artigarvan Primary School

FORDS

F   ast and fabulous cars
O   gre engines
R   acing wheels
D   rift them if you dare
S   ideways all the time.

Peter Riddles (11)
Artigarvan Primary School

PIXIE

I have a pony called Pixie
I feed her every day
And at the weekend when she's out
Running, trotting and jumping about,
I give her a shout!
'It's time to come in, I've mucked you out.
I bedded your stable and filled your trough
With all your goodies, so you don't catch a cough!'
She's a very good pony and never sad,
For when I come to see her, she's always glad.

Lesley Wallace (11)
Artigarvan Primary School

WASTE

W onderful world being destroyed by waste.
A ction needs to be taken
S eriously by everyone.
T hink of what you're doing to the world.
E veryone needs to stand up to waste!

Jordan Burke (11)
Artigarvan Primary School

A PUPPY

When I saw that little puppy,
I thought she wasn't ours,
I asked my dad who she belonged to,
Can we keep her for evermore?

So off we go out to the shops,
To buy her lots of stuff,
With the trolley packed up to the rim,
Dad frowns and says, 'That's quite enough.'

We named our puppy Sophie,
She's so cute, playful and fun,
We're so happy that we kept her,
That's my little puppy.

Andrea Parkhill (11)
Artigarvan Primary School

WRESTLING

W restling is my favourite sport.
R aw is my favourite wrestling show.
E dge is the best wrestler.
S trong men.
T ough fighters.
L ucky victories.
I ncredible strength.
N ervous fighters.
G igantic men.

Nathan King (11)
Artigarvan Primary School

LIVERPOOL

L iverpool
I s
V ery
E nergetic
R eds
P laying
O n
O ld Trafford
L and.

Joel Hutchinson (11)
Artigarvan Primary School

SCHOOL DAYS

Monday I hate
because I'm always late.
Tuesday I was taught
how a football is caught.
Wednesday I got lines
for being so pretty and fine.
Thursday I got a test
but I didn't do my best.
Friday is the end of the week
and the weekend I will seek.

Cheryl Scott (11)
Artigarvan Primary School

GARETH GATES

G   reat
A   mazing
R   ehearsals
E   legant
T   welfth of July (birthday)
H   andsome

G   areth-mania
A   uditions
T   alented musician
E   ligible
S   tammer.

Rebecca Thompson (11)
Artigarvan Primary School

WHOSE DOOR?

Every night-time in our class
A new world appears
Through the trapdoor, near the roof
New creatures, a place of fears

At break time, while we're eating
I glance up now and then
I know more creatures come out at night
But they will not tell us when

During the daytime
The door is shut tight
But when school time is over
Out come the creatures of night

I never have seen them
But I know they're there
They're slimy and creepy
With huge eyes and no hair!

They play in the roof space
In the old water tank
They'd soak you and drown you
And all for a prank

While we are doing our lessons
I know where they are
Through a crack in the trapdoor
They peep out after dark . . .

Tracey Lawn (11)
Derrychrin Primary School

MY COUSIN, KYRA

My cousin, Kyra is the shiny colour gold,
The sunny season summer or even a mighty forest,
                                adventurous and bold.
A quick jolt of lightning that strikes over my head,
She's the place where I dream in, the place called bed.
To me, she's that funny tabby Garfield, (only much thinner),
She's the cake on my plate that I rarely get for dinner.
An aqua speedy Volkswagen,
A great flying sky dragon.
She's even the lifesaver water,
She's a volcano before it's about to erupt,
But more importantly she's my mum's brother's daughter.

Mona Younes (11)
Derrychrin Primary School

A GRUESOME POEM

Dead men walking
Fat birds talking
Crippled men coughing
Yellow pigs snorting
Little toddlers sulking
Mean men stealing from the poor
Mincemeat, chopped meat, smelly meat
Fly-infested pork!
Cool? Certainly not!
I warn you not to come to this place
Where the spooks and ghouls of the night
Are sure to give you
A gruesome fright!

Joseph Hurl (11)
Derrychrin Primary School

A DOOR INTO THE DARK

At the end of our street
There's an old spooky house
Nobody lives there
Not even a mouse

At night we go past it
The old gate lies broken
The windowpane's cracked
And the front door's wide open

Behind, there is darkness
Stairs lead up the hall
There are bugs, bats and insects
And they crawl on the wall

To push the door wide
To enter this place
Needs courage and bravery
It's a place hard to face

Who would have lived here
A long time ago?
Some children? Their parents?
We will never know

I'd like to go further
To go through the door
I may find some answers
If I could explore

Maybe someday
You will never know
I might live there
And explore the show.

Emma McIvor (10)
Derrychrin Primary School

MY BIG SISTERS

My sister loves to dance
Loves make-up and small pants
Love the boys
Makes lots of noise
That's my big sister number one

My sister loves to cook
Tries to poison me with her food
She likes to read quite a lot
With Harry Potter she's lost the plot
That's my big sister number two

My sister is a hot-tempered bull
You'll never get her to keep her cool
And Internet freak, surfing every day of the week
That's my big sister number three

Now we have number four
The one adults all adore
No one mentioned number four
Because that little someone's me!

Paula McNeill (11)
Derrychrin Primary School

THE DOOR

It looks very scary,
Yet something pushes me on,
I see a door, it's tall, strong and very old,
But there's a small knob just the right size for me,
I stop and think what's inside,
Why, it might be a giant
Or an ogre waiting to eat me.

Why, it might be a hobbit or even an elf,
Maybe, just maybe,
I go up to the door and twist the knob
And wait for a moment,
I thought I saw something move in the gloom,
I just swung it wider and it was a . . .

Owen Devlin (10)
Derrychrin Primary School

DOORS

In the middle of the wood,
Stands a tiny door,
Inside a fearful creature,
With blood on the floor,
I look through his keyhole,
Where has he gone?
The door swings open,
So I tiptoe on,
He is still out of sight,
So I peep round his house,
As I go upstairs,
The door crashes open,
I run downstairs
And stare him straight,
A shock awaits me,
A creature ugly and fierce,
Roars and bellows and comes at me,
I am lucky to get out,
I am never opening that door again.

Tony Martin (10)
Derrychrin Primary School

COME

Come with me to a magical place,
where fairies frolic and pixies chase.
Come with me and stay for evermore,
behind a bush is an enchanted door.

Over the hills and far away,
is where the leprechauns and kelpies play.
Where the freezing winter is no more,
through a magical enchanted door.

Merrily the phoenixes play,
their fiery tails burn brightly each day
and at night there are moons that light your way,
behind a door that's hidden away.

Everyone's waiting so please rush,
you'll find the door behind a rosebush.
So hurry up and come today,
through the door that's hidden far away.

Shereen Younes (11)
Derrychrin Primary School

THE GREEN DOOR

I see a door,
A large, green, round door,
I wonder what's inside?
It looks to be a magical creature,
Staring through the keyhole at me.

I see a door,
I think I might open it,
If it doesn't scare,
But I think it will not,
I hope . . .

I see a door,
It could conceal a goblin,
Or a hobgoblin, or supposedly just a hobbit,
The friendliest of all creatures,
That a door could conceal.

Daniel McKinless (10)
Derrychrin Primary School

A New Dimension

Playing in the old house
With my little dog,
An old door, splintered and rotten,
A jar at the end of the hall,
Light from behind it
Lured me on further,
One push, the door disintegrates,
Instead a round, metal porthole faced me,
A wheel to open,
Inside, a glowing light
Reveals a chute leading down,
Twisting and bending,
A roller coaster ride,
A bumpy jolt stops me
And my little dog,
We're now in a new world,
Alien and strange,
All metal and shiny,
Tiny dwarf-like humanoids,
Do they speak my language?
I might never know,
How will I even
Return to my home?

Noelle Devlin (11)
Derrychrin Primary School

WHOSE DOOR?

I was staring at a door ten feet tall,
I looked through the keyhole and what did I see?
A big orange eye looking at me.
Whose door?

I open the door, I say, I say!
With a clatter, a bang and a crash,
A big ugly giant looking at me!
Arrrgghhhh!
Whose door?

He looked straight in my face
And said, 'Get out of here!'
I ran as fast as I could,
But I stopped at his door and I . . .
Woke up in my own room,
Staring at . . . *my door!*

Kyle Loughran (11)
Derrychrin Primary School

THE DOOR!

A rainy day; pitter-patter of raindrops,
Interrupted by my bell tinkling in the rain.
A long, tall human; fair and young and lost.

A voice sweet and clear; no need to fear.
My little door squeaked and stretched to fit!

One world's creature visiting another!
When the rain had stopped my visitor squeezed
Off home; a giant on her own, but not so bad
    After all.

Geraldine McVey (10)
Derrychrin Primary School

A DOOR ALL ALONE

A door was all alone,
I didn't see anybody, absolutely no one.
It didn't look scary,
But the spiders were hairy.

When I got near,
I felt a lot of fear.
I wonder what could be in there?
Maybe a lion or a bear?

It was very old
And when I opened it, I felt a chill of cold.
'Hello, good day to you.'
'It's cold in here, I hope I don't catch the flu.'
'Come over here to the fire, it will make your temperature higher.'

He was very, very hairy,
But not quite scary.
His feathers were like a big gown
And he was hanging upside down.
He was sitting in the corner of the shed,
He had big red ears on his head.

I wasn't going to suddenly flee,
He wasn't about to kill me.
Just a strange old man alone in a shed,
Or an evil creature; one of the undead!

Karl McKinless (11)
Derrychrin Primary School

NIGHTMARE

He is wild and free in the forest,
But only out at night,
In your mind he feeds on animals,
But a child's soft skin's his delight.

This thing that lives inside of you,
Whom you are frightened to sleep by,
Is the king of nightmares,
That nobody has seen.

Tonight his eyes are crimson,
Tonight his face is mouldy,
His claws are as sharp as a dagger's blade
And his body is huge and hairy.

Tomorrow night you'll have a scare,
To find him hiding in your hair,
Clinging on for all his might,
But that's all for tomorrow night!

Hugh Henry (11)
Derrychrin Primary School

WHATIF

(Based on 'Whatif' by Shel Silverstein)

W hatif a spider crawled in my ear?
H igh in the sky ghosts fly
A t night I was surrounded by them
T he night-time whatifs strike again
I was scared out of my wits
F ly away and escape the whatifs!

Melissa McCann (8)
Edendork Primary School

WHATIF

(Based on 'Whatif' by Shel Silverstein)

Last night while I lay thinking,
Some whatifs visited me.

Whatif my teeth were not white?
Whatif my eyes could not see
Whatif my friends did not like me?
Whatif I did not go to bed at night?
Whatif my pet was a white rat?
Whatif pink hair was on my head?
Whatif I love you was never said?
Whatif my house was not a home?

Everything seems swell and then the night-time,
Whatifs strike again.

Nicola McNally (9)
Edendork Primary School

A GIRL'S HEAD

Inside my head
I like the colour red

I often sit and think
I like Slush Puppies to drink

Sometimes when I am alone
I am glad I am at home

I go horse riding two days of the week
But I think of it every day of the week.

Niamh Faloon (9)
Edendork Primary School

ME

S inéad is my name,
I n to dolls and reading is my game,
N ever slow to do my work,
E ven when I get too much,
A lways there for my friends,
D oing chores, oh, it never ends.

C hocolate is my favourite treat,
U nfortunately it's bad for my teeth,
R ed is my favourite colour,
R oller skating, I just can't be bothered,
I nside the room, I dance away, but
E ach fine day I'm out to play.

Sinéad Currie (8)
Edendork Primary School

ME

J ust a boy
O nly eight
S miling every day
E ven in school
P laying with my friends
H appiest at football

Q uite good at it
U seless at washing the dishes
I 'm smart
N ot dumb!
N o matter what anyone says.

Joseph Quinn (8)
Edendork Primary School

MY DAD

My dad is fun,
He never looks glum.
When I go out to play,
He comes out to say,
'Come in for tea,
You are a crazy bee!'
I say, 'No,'
And he says, 'Now, go!'
I go inside
And do what I'm told.
That's because . . .
I'm not very old!
My dad is fun,
He never looks glum.

Aidan McKenna (8)
Edendork Primary School

ABOUT ME

G iggling and laughing at funny things,
E xcited at what the day will bring.
M y friends are funny,
M y friends are kind,
A lways there, always mine.

W herever I go,
E veryone is there,
I n my heart for the
R est of the day.

Gemma Weir (9)
Edendork Primary School

I COULD HAVE GONE . . .

My mum went for a walk tonight,
In the rain!
I could have gone,
But 'The Simpsons' was on.
She walked into the town
And she walked out again.
I could have gone,
But 'The Simpsons' was on.
In she came,
Wet from head to toe.
I could have gone,
But I'm glad 'The Simpsons' were on!

Gillan Lavery (9)
Edendork Primary School

ME

M aking music on the piano
A nd listening to my favourite CD
R eading the pages of 'Vicky Angel'
Y ummy, it's curry and chips for tea

C uddling up to Max (the cuddly dog)
O h! How I hate a long car journey
N ever mind, I love going to Granny's house
L ove going shopping with her
A lways sure to get something nice
N o one luckier than me.

Mary Conlan (9)
Edendork Primary School

MUM GOT MAD

Mum and me
Mum and me
Mum got mad
And threw a pie at me!
She got kind and generous
And threw another pie at me!
I said, 'Yum, yum, yum -
It tastes like bubblegum -
Can you do that again?'
She got angry and mad
She said, 'Go to the sitting room!'
Then she was really
Mad!

Simon McNally (9)
Edendork Primary School

ME AND MY FRIENDS

With me and my friends
The fun never ends,
Karsan and Ciaran kicking the ball around,
Everyone getting dirty on the ground.
Listening to music, carrying on,
Listening to CDs all night long.
We also have our school friends,
Which makes you want school to never end.
We all have a good time with our friends,
But eventually it has to end.

Lorcán McGrath (9)
Edendork Primary School

MY SECRET PET

I was walking down
In the woods one day,
I saw a bush
Move away.
I caught it
And guess what I saw?
A big head and tiny little claws.
I took it out,
It was all so white.
A little snow teddy,
He glowed all night.
I told him,
'Stay there,
Don't come with me.'
So I ran home
To get my tea,
But when I returned -
He was gone
In a rush.
The little snow teddy
I found in the bush.

Clara Dorman (9)
Edendork Primary School

TRASH

Trash has nothing to do with life,
Wriggling in the wind,
As sharp as a knife.

A simple thing,
Just throw it away,
Sometimes the wind
Just blows it away.

Hidden in
The night-time's heart,
Trash lies hidden
In the dark.

Thomas Hislop (8)
Edendork Primary School

MY DIARY ON JUNE 7TH

First had sports day
Fell in front of the finish line!

The cross teacher who spits in your face
When he talks and you're drenched!
Gave us homework for the next term.

Got served drool for dinner and all,
At lunch I had to leave the kitchen
Because of my teacher's spit!

Went to the cinema with my friends,
Who always laugh at me
Because of me being wet
(Because of the teacher's spit),
Said to my friends,
'I hate our new teacher,
He spits on you!'

Mr Woldefidle was right behind us,
(He heard us)
And after the film I ran
As fast as I could home.

Well now I have got a future at school.

My diary on June 7th.

Tom McKernan (9)
Edendork Primary School

DOWN IN THE DUMP

Down in the
     Dump
    Is lots
     Of
    Treasure.
  Mummy thinks
     It is
   Ridiculous!
     But every
       Other kid
      In the
      School
    Loves to search
     For
    Old wheels,
    Mobiles,
     Bikes.
Wouldn't you
    Search for
    Treasure
     Down in
       The dump?

Macaulay Dillon (9)
Edendork Primary School

ME

As strong as an ox
I can really box

As big as an elephant
I can blow out of my trunk

As fast as a cheetah
I can race past a car

As tall as a giraffe
I can see over trees

As smart as an ant
I plan to lift big rocks

As swift as an eagle
That is me, Mark!

Mark Bullock (9)
Edendork Primary School

WHEN I WAS FIVE

When I was five
I wanted a pet - I asked
My mum
If I could have a pet
She said
Not yet -
Not yet -
Not yet!

`Now I am 10 -
I have just made
A wooden cage -
And I have a pet
To put inside

He keeps me
Happy
When I feel sad
He is a mouse
And I call him
Jerry.

Olivia McGrath (8)
Edendork Primary School

BARNEY

Barney is my friend,
Although he can't talk,
He can walk,
Though on all fours!

I take him for walks,
On his special lead,
Sometimes he tugs
And sometimes he leads.

Barney is special,
As special as can be,
Although he is tiny,
He's a big dog to me!

Barney is a super dog,
The best there can ever be!
He is my best friend,
He will never leave me.

Katie Jane Rooney (9)
Edendork Primary School

LOVE IS . . .

Love is caring . . .
Love is sharing . . .
Love is playing
With my friends.
Love is helping
Those who are sick.
Love is caring . . .
Love is sharing.

Thomas Mulgrew (9)
Edendork Primary School

MY FRIEND

I have a friend called Conleth
He sits beside me in class
He helps me in my work
And when I am unhappy
He cheers me up
When I have a good idea
He pats me on the back
One day I was in the town
And he and I
Had a Big Mac
He's some craic, my friend,
Conleth.

Adam Burns (9)
Edendork Primary School

MY PET DOG

My dog's name is
Shadow,
He lives in a den.
He sits and sniffs
And sometimes he chews
My pens!
I give him food and water,
He keeps me happy every day.
But most of all,
I love him,
That's what he's for,
Anyway!

Sarah Dooey (9)
Edendork Primary School

TXT TLK

Txtng, txtng
txtng al arnd
txtng hr
txtng thr
ths, tht
txtng, txtng
txtng arnd
txt me hr, thr
evywre
ltttts
txtng tlk
txtng hm, hr
txtng tlk!

Joseph Daly (9)
Edendork Primary School

SNOWFLAKES

S nowflakes, snowflakes falling everywhere,
N o one hates the snowflake's stare,
O oh how it makes us shiver!
W hat shall we do, for winter is here?
F alling, falling to the ground, I wonder how it makes no sound?
L ook how the ground's white,
A h, I'll have a snowball fight,
K icking the snow, here I come, get ready!
E asy peasy, let's go play.

Jade Quinn (9)
Edendork Primary School

MUM

My mum is fun,
She never looks glum,
Every time she makes us food,
It always tastes
Yum! Yum! Yum!
Sometimes she goes for a run.
That's my mum,
She never acts dumb!
My mum is fun.

Jessica McGonigle (9)
Edendork Primary School

WINTER

Sparkling, gleaming snow creeps over the land once again,
The trees are bare like skeletons decorated with a splutter
                                    of white powder.
Everything around seems to be asleep
And Mr Frost comes to make it even colder,
Breathing his icy breath over the land
But makes beautiful patterns on our windows.
My own breath is like steam coming out of a kettle
And my nose and fingers are numb and red with cold.
The snowmen are being dressed up by children
With a hat, scarf and carrot,
Which is all that is left behind when the winter sun
Peeps out from behind the clouds.

Eimear O'Donnell (10)
Evish Primary School

WINTER

Winter is here with us again,
The children running through the cold cotton snow.
The trees look like skeletons with bits of snow covering their arms.
Jack Frost casts his icy spells over our windows,
Leaving sparkly patterns that look like delicate embroidery.
The festive season is here,
Children take great delight in the fun and games
That the winter brings.

Ciaran McDaid (9)
Evish Primary School

WAR IS . . .

War is like a demon rising from Hell.
War looks like a man called
the Grim Reaper collecting souls.
It sounds like a volcano erupting
and it can be a lethal epidemic,
but it always seems to stay
around somewhere.

Barry McMackin (11)
Evish Primary School

ALLITERATION WITH THE LETTER 'P'

Pat the polar bear put on a party
And pumped and pranced with
Paddy the potty seal.
Polar bear went out, pumped his legs,
Looked back and that's when he hit the pole!

Peter Farrell (9)
Evish Primary School

WINTER

Winter is here now,
Bringing us icicles and a blanket of white,
Soft, falling snow which looks like fluffy, soft cotton.
Jack Frost breathes his icy breath on our windows
In the mornings
And he leaves behind dangling icicles to decorate our rooftops.
Inside, families huddle around the front of the blazing fire,
Thinking about what they'll put into the Christmas stockings.
Animals also stay inside
And find it easy to sleep,
During this calm and serene season,
Given to us by Jesus Christ,
Born on Christmas Day.

Kevin Farrell (9)
Evish Primary School

AUTUMN

Autumn, I wish you would've
Let summer stay a little bit longer,
I know you bring the harvest but
I wish you wouldn't bring long,
Dull days too!
Evenings fall dark quickly
And are spooky,
But I do like the different
Coloured leaves that I shuffle
Beneath my feet.

Anton McGrinder (10)
Evish Primary School

Autumn

Sad autumn children
have to stay inside
because of the cold
wet weather.

Happy autumn loves
children crunching
through the leaves.

Worried autumn
drivers are scared
in case trees fall
on them.

Dylan Flanagan (9)
Evish Primary School

Autumn

Hello autumn, goodbye summer,
I'll miss your warm sun and all the happiness it brought.
But now I can hear the leaves talking to me
As I walk along the brown carpet,
Rustling and crunching like a packet of crisps.
When the cold, rushing wind is angry,
The woodlands lose their leaves quickly
And they weep as if they'd lost their beloved friends.
Maybe it's the witches and wizards
Casting their mystery and magic at this time of year.

Keelin Stewart (9)
Evish Primary School

WINTER

One day I made a snowman,
I gave him a big hat.
He had coal for eyes
And his belly was really fat.

A blanket of snow covered the ground,
Snowflakes fell without a sound.
In winter robins came out in search of food,
A little hedgehog slept under a plank of wood.

Jack Frost came out each wintry night,
He covered the gardens in a sheet of white.
Hungry robins came flying by,
As snow fell from the cold, cold sky.

Aodhain McDaid (8)
Evish Primary School

WINTER

Winter is back again,
Snowflakes are swaying delicately to the ground below
Which is covered in soft white snow.
Jack Frost is out and about casting cold spells outside,
Freezing everything in his path.
Trees are bare, hanging loosely like old skeletons,
But it's not all gloom -
As we decorate our homes for the festive period.
Families come together again to remember
And celebrate this important time of year.

Marvina Lynch (11)
Evish Primary School

Alliteration With The Letter 'F'

Fred, the flat, fussy fish from Finland,
Flipped from the freezing water
Into a French boat that took him to a fair.
He made a friend and found some food
And sat beside a fire.
From that day on, he was no longer only a flat fish,
But a flat fish that was fried and eaten!

Danica Conway (10)
Evish Primary School

War Is . . .

War is like a raging bull
running to a red rag.
It looks like an ugly tormentor.
It sounds like loud shrieks
and drums with banshees
and it can ruin lives forever,
but it won't seem to go away.

Rachel Boggs (9)
Evish Primary School

Winter

The children play on a cold winter day,
until all the cold snow melts away.

The cold winds arrive and they shall blow,
in and out of houses they will go.

I like to slip and play on the ice,
but when I fall it isn't nice.

The twinkling snowflakes are falling down without a sound,
softly they land all over the snow-covered ground.

As the winter wind blows its cold, frosty air,
it makes the trees all cold and bare.

Hayley Doherty (9)
Evish Primary School

WINTER

Children love to wake up and see
the snow on the ground
and look at the patterns left
on their windows.
The cold makes me feel numb
and turns me red and purple,
when I walk on a cotton wool blanket.
At night I love to snuggle up
in front of a big fire,
to get away from the cross winter wind.

Killian Lynch (9)
Evish Primary School

SPRING

Springtime is here again.
The sun is shining up in the sky.
The lambs are skipping,
The calves are jumping.
The daffodils are sprouting
And snowdrops too.
Oh what a beautiful season this is.

Megan Donnell (9)
Gortin Primary School

THE GOLDEN JUBILEE

The Golden Jubilee
Everyone is happy!

There are . . .

Flags waving in the air
Banners flying high

The National Anthem can be heard
Today the Queen is here
People having parties in the street
You know who they want to meet
The Queen!

The Golden Jubilee is here
Everyone will shout and cheer!

Andrew Baxter (11)
Gortin Primary School

A TIME TO . . .

For everything there is a season
And a time for every matter under Heaven

There is a time to play, a time to rest.
There is a time to run, a time to skip.
There is a time to say hello, a time to say goodbye.
There is a time for dinner, a time for tea.
There is a time to go to bed, a time to wake up.

Bryony Houston (10)
Gortin Primary School

SPRINGTIME

Spring, spring
It is spring
Birds are singing songs
New baby lambs are
Being born.

Rabbits are jumping
Away in the grass
Chicks are hatching
And they are being born.

Happy, happy spring.

Rebecca Kennedy (9)
Gortin Primary School

SONG OF THE RAINFOREST

Follow! Follow!
We shall follow the Yanomamis,
Up the trees, down the plants,
We shall follow on,
Through the trees, through the plants,
We are all scared,
We could get cut down any minute,
Monkeys, monkeys singing in the treetops,
Let your branches shake high,
If you do not help us, we will die.

Aaron Campbell (10)
Gortin Primary School

THE GOLDEN JUBILEE

The Golden Jubilee
Has finally come
There's . . .
Dancing in the street
Flags are flying high
The Queen is coming around
And that is what is happening
At the Golden Jubilee.

Kyle McIlwaine (10)
Gortin Primary School

A TIME TO . . .

For everything there is a season
And a time for every matter under Heaven

A time to fall asleep and a time to wake up
A time to talk and a time to listen
A time to eat sweets and a time to go to the dentist
A time to fall and a time to jump
A time to rule and a time to obey
A time to go crazy and a time to calm down.

Andrew Kane (9)
Gortin Primary School

MOBILE PHONE

My boyfriend has a mobile phone
Now we don't get a minute alone
When I ask him for a kiss
He says, 'Wait until I answer this!'

If you're looking for a boyfriend
My advice to you would be
If he has a mobile phone
Don't bother about him
Just leave him alone!

Jade Baxter (8)
Gortin Primary School

A TIME TO . . .

For everything there is a season
And a time for every matter under Heaven

A time to grow and a time to harvest.
A time to cut and a time to bale.
A time to start and a time to stop.
A time to buy and a time to sell.
A time to sleep and a time to wake up.
A time to write and a time to finish.

Adam McFarland (10)
Gortin Primary School

THE WIND

As I make the trees sway,
They bow down to me, the master,
Anyone who disobeys me,
I lift them up and toss them about.

As I lift the roofs off houses, I roar,
People need to catch their hats in my cold breeze.

Lauren McFarland (10)
Gortin Primary School

THE SNAKE WHO ATE MY MOUSE

One day I found a snake
Lying on the floor,
First it looked at me and then it saw my mouse
Over by the door.

It slithered over the carpet,
It slithered over a wellie
And now my pet mouse
Is in that snake's belly.

Now I have no pet mouse
I've only got this snake,
I swear someday,
I'll cut its head off with a rake.

Now I have no pet mouse,
Nor do I have a snake,
Now all I have
Is that old, grey rake.

Adam Fleming (10)
Gortin Primary School

A TIME TO . . .

For everything there is a season
And a time for every matter under Heaven.

A time to laugh, a time to weep.
A time to plant, a time to reap.
A time to sing, a time to pray.
A time to eat sweets, a time to go to the dentist.
A time to love, a time to hate.
A time to tear, a time to mend.

Kathryn Beattie (10)
Gortin Primary School

A Time To . . .

For everything there is a season
And a time for every matter under Heaven

A time to play
A time to work
A time to eat
A time to drink
A time to live
A time to die
A time to sleep
A time to wake
A time to laugh
A time to mourn.

Ashley Whelan (11)
Gortin Primary School

Time To . . .

For everything there is a season
And a time for every matter under Heaven

A time to run
A time to walk
A time to kill
A time to drink
A time to eat
A time to wake
A time to sleep
A time to work
A time to play
A time to draw.

Robert McIlwaine (8)
Gortin Primary School

A Time To . . .

For everything there is a season
And a time for ev'ry matter under Heaven.

A time to eat and a time to drink,
A time to play and a time to work,
A time to sleep and a time to wake,
A time to buy and a time to sell,
A time to come and a time to go,
A time to start and a time to stop,
A time to break and a time to fix,
A time to be new and a time to be old,
A time to talk and a time to be silent,
A time to play and a time to relax.

Alan Nesbitt (10)
Gortin Primary School

A Time To . . .

For ev'rything there is a season
And a time for ev'ry matter under Heaven

A time to make and a time to bake
A time to write, a time to mark
A time to go out, a time to come in
A time to open, a time to close
A time to go, a time to stop
A time to get up, a time to get down
A time to read, a time to draw.

Jason Fleming (9)
Gortin Primary School

IN THE GARDEN

In the garden
Daffodil dancing
In the cool days
Of spring

In the garden
Sunflowers sunbathing
In the hot days
Of summer

In the garden
Leaves leaving
In the windy days
Of autumn

In the garden
Snow spreading
In frosty days
Of winter.

Lisa McFarland (9)
Gortin Primary School

MY FAMILY

F   is for family,
A   is for always together,
M   is for Mum,
I   is for in the house all day long,
L   is for love,
Y   is for sometimes yelling.

Gavin Tummon (9)
Loughash Primary School

SHEEP

Sheep are my favourite animals of all,
They gather around at my shepherd's call.

Blackface, Cheviot and Texel to name but a few,
Famous for wool and delicious mutton too.

Working with them can be tough but funny,
If they breed well you'll earn lots of money.

As you enter the show to compete with the best,
You're hoping for number one, over the rest.

Log on to 'Black Face Breeders' site and see,
The Loughash 'Blackies' for they belong to me.

Cathal Harkin (10)
Loughash Primary School

MY FAVOURITE THINGS

My favourite sport is football,
My favourite team is Ireland.
My favourite footballer is Robbie Keane.

My favourite food is chicken curry,
My favourite cereal is Nesquick.

My favourite car is a Subaru,
My favourite console is the PS2,
My favourite pet is a dog.

My favourite colour is blue,
My favourite subject is PE,
My best friend is Cathal.

Ryan Tummon (10)
Loughash Primary School

ANIMALS

I like animals, I hope you do too,
I like the sound of the cow saying *moo*.

I like the sound when the horse says neigh,
I always hear her say it when I give her some hay.

I like the kitten with her tiny little claws,
But you better be careful with her big jaws.

I like the piglets because they're nice and pink,
But you better block your nose because they really stink.

I like the ducklings because they're covered with fluff,
But they can get in trouble with my dog, Scruff.

I have a dog and his name is Scruff,
Sometimes he is rough on Muff.

Claire Knox (8)
Loughash Primary School

MY FAMILY

My family are so loving and caring,
Forever giving and always sharing.
Now and then they drive me mad
And on occasions make me sad.
Even so we love each other
And really adore our father and mother.
I am so happy when they're around,
My feet they seldom touch the ground.

Sinead Kerlin (10)
Loughash Primary School

FOOTBALL

My favourite game is football,
I play it every day
And when I score a tricky goal,
I shout, 'Hip hip hooray!'

Football is a brilliant game,
It helps to keep me fit.
I feel as good as Owen,
When I put on my kit.

Whenever I am busy
And don't have time to play,
You'll find me at the TV,
Enjoying 'Match of the Day'.

I dream I'll be a football star,
When I grow up
And lead my country on the pitch
And win the World Cup.

Michael O'Neill (10)
Loughash Primary School

MY DAD

My dad to me is a very kind friend
And he loves his children to the end.
He's kindly, generous and always caring,
At birthdays and Christmas he's forever sharing.
My dad makes sure we get what we need,
He even gets nuts for the cows to feed.
To me, my dad is definitely the best,
He helped me through my transfer test.

Susan McGaughey (11)
Loughash Primary School

MY PET

I have a pet called Sally,
She's fluffy and furry
And loves to scurry.
She jumps about,
But does not shout,
I buy her food but she'd rather have grass,
Why? I don't know but I dare not ask.
She stays in a hutch at the front of the house
And she has a friend - a little field mouse.
She's my black and white rabbit
And has no bad habit.
She keeps herself neat,
When in danger she bangs her feet.
The cat looks into her hutch,
But she'd better not touch,
My pet rabbit called Sally.

Ailish Hood (10)
Loughash Primary School

MY ROOM

M   y room has two single beds
Y   awning on my bed I lie

R   esting for a little while
O   nly me and my TV
O   ffers me a place to be
M   e in my little room.

Patrick Harkin (8)
Loughash Primary School

DIFFERENT PEOPLE

Some people are big, but some are small,
Some people are short, but some are tall.
Everybody has a different like,
Some playing football or cycling their bike.

Some cheeks are white or red like roses,
Some have pointed or wee fat noses.
With hair of brown, black and red,
Some straight or curly, or even a skinhead.

Lots of freckles dotted around,
Eyes of blue, green and brown.
Some have short sight, some have long,
With glasses or contacts to help them along.

With skin of white, black or yellow,
Priest or teacher, girl or fellow.
They are parts of God's work of art,
Millions of people since the very start.

So whenever you meet people be slow to judge,
Give them a smile and don't hold a grudge.
Everyone is needed both good and bad,
Without all these people it sure would be sad.

Leona Feeney (11)
Loughash Primary School

MY BEST FRIEND

My best friend is really caring,
Her and me are always sharing.
Every day we laugh and sing,
We're just best friends at everything.

If we ever have a fight,
I tell my mum, 'I don't feel right,'
She says, 'Just go and say you're sorry,
Be friends and you won't have to worry.'

Aideen Traynor (9)
Loughash Primary School

SCHOOLDAYS

I love going to my local school,
Where all my friends are really cool.
We laugh and play and have lots of fun,
But still we manage to get work done.

Master Blee is our senior teacher so fine,
We never talk or walk out of line.
Mrs Carlin teaches the junior classes well,
We often long to be under her spell.

We have to add, subtract and sometimes divide
And write long stories about 'life' outside.
Once a week we go swimming and have PE,
We all love it here, my friends and me.

We all like to run and bounce a ball,
We sometimes shout and often call.
When you're sick or have a really bad cough,
Master Blee will always let you off.

When it's winter with all the frost and snow
And heating's off so home we go,
But summer days are the best of all,
Because you don't have school at all.

Ciara Devine (9)
Loughash Primary School

MY FRIEND

There's someone for whom I really care,
With her my sweets I'll always share.
Friends like her are hard to find,
She's never cheeky, she's always kind.

Through every month through all the seasons,
She's my best friend for lots of reasons.
We phone each other every night
And say, 'Sweet dreams' and 'Do sleep tight.'

I hope we'll always stay this way
And see each other every day.
I'm really glad I told my mother
That Aideen and I met each other.

Mary Kerlin (9)
Loughash Primary School

LUCKY

Lucky the dog is as daft as can be,
She's fond of Alannah and quite fond of me.
She jumps up and down and makes a great fuss,
When Kevin and I get off the school bus.
She has very long legs and when she sits down,
Her legs are spread out all over the ground.

Her mum's name is Speedy and she has a bad chest
And all she can do is breathe loudly and rest.
I wish that Lucky could live on forever,
She's a special dog and she's very clever.

Sherilyn Phillips (9)
Loughash Primary School

PLEASE MR BUSH!

People think a war will start,
When the inspectors do depart,
But Mr Bush please hold your fire,
To slaughter children we don't desire.
The Iraqi people have done nothing wrong,
There're better ways to prove you're strong.
To wait and talk you think it's silly,
But we all think you are a bully.
If you occupy Iraqi soil,
The world will know it is for their oil.
I beg you, please don't go too far,
You might just start a worldwide war.

Maureen Dooher (9)
Loughash Primary School

HOLIDAYS

H olidays are the greatest time of year,
O rganising and packing, it's coming near.
L ots of sunshine, sea and sand,
I love France, it's really grand.
D ancing and splashing around the pool
A nd some ice cream to keep us cool.
Y elling and screaming as we go over the waves,
S ightseeing and going to visit the caves.

Genevieve Feeney (9)
Loughash Primary School

SUMMER HOLIDAYS

I like the summer holidays,
The weather's such a peach,
I get to go to the seaside
And build castles on the beach.

There's lots of lovely ice cream,
You can picnic on the grass,
You can slide down the helter-skelter
And wave at friends that pass.

There are trampolines for jumping on,
I think they're really great
And when it isn't raining,
I get out my board and skate.

But best of all there's no alarm,
To wake me up at eight,
I'm on my summer holidays,
So I can stay up late!

Kevin Moran (10)
Loughash Primary School

RUBBISH

Rubbish, rubbish
On the ground
Cans, bottles and papers too
Streets and parks and public loos
Please pick it up after you.

Oonagh Harkin (8)
Loughash Primary School

MY FRIENDS

Friends are so nice,
Friends are good fun,
Friends are helpful when the day's begun.
With friends in my childhood and the great games we play,
With laughter and joy throughout our school day.
Without my kind friends I would have no pleasure,
As they help me along in this world -
They're a treasure.

Ann-Marie Crossan (9)
Loughash Primary School

FRIENDS AND FAMILY

My mum and I took our dog for a walk,
We stopped at my friend's for a talk.
Mum said, 'We'll get on our way,'
Then I said, 'Bye, I'll see you another day.'

We stopped at the Spar,
Mum bought me a bar.
I gave Mum a bit,
She really enjoyed it.

We went back home,
We really enjoyed our roam.

I think I'll go again tomorrow.

Kirsty McGarvey (9)
St Brigid's Primary School, Cranagh

MY DOG, GLEN

I have a dog, his name is Glen,
I chose this name, as it rhymes with Ben.
Glen, he is very funny,
Most of the time he hops like a bunny.
Glen, he is very fast,
When he's racing me he flies past.
Glen, he can never be caught,
Everyone thinks he's pretty hot.
Glen, he loves to play,
If he could, he'd play all day.
Glen he's truly the best,
He can always beat the rest.
Glen the dog, he's very fine,
But best of all he's *mine*.

Conor McGarvey (10)
St Brigid's Primary School, Cranagh

MY FRIEND

My best friend is Ciara, we always have some fun,
But when we are racing, she has lots and lots of fun.
Her hair is long and very blonde,
She is very good at sport,
She likes other subjects too.
Her favourite colours are red and blue,
Her favourite animal is a dog.
She takes care of all of them
And she likes frogs.

Denise Conway (10)
St Brigid's Primary School, Cranagh

My Family

My family is the best,
better than all the rest.
If the weather is mild,
they let me play on the slide.
If I did something bad,
they wouldn't be mad.
They gave me money,
to buy a cute bunny.
They let my friend come to our house,
just to play with our pet mouse.
I have the best family in the world.

Caroline Mc Connell (11)
St Brigid's Primary School, Cranagh

My Family

My daddy loves brandy,
He drinks it every week.
I always say he should give it up,
He only giggles and laughs.
My mummy is so kind,
I love her so, so much.
My brothers are so noisy,
They drive me crazy.
My granny lives at 214,
She always cleans and brushes the floor.
I love my family.

Kevin Conway (10)
St Brigid's Primary School, Cranagh

WORST BEST FRIENDS

Me and my friend are the worst best friends you could meet,
Under the table we mess about and kick with our feet.
He is like the brother I never had,
When we are together, we go mad.

We are rough-and-tumble boys,
We fight over each other's toys.
We are in the same class
And we are as bold as brass.

The teacher sees us as a mortal threat,
Our parents are the same I bet.
In fields we go exploring,
We both think school is so boring!

We drive our mothers up the walls,
We break and smash our sister's dolls.
We may not be clever,
But we're the best friends ever.

Ryan Falls (9)
St Brigid's Primary School, Cranagh

MY FRIEND

My friend is top of the class,
When the 11+ is here, he will probably pass,
But still my friend is the best,
Better than the rest.

When you're playing a game with him,
He would probably win.
When Kieran is about,
He always wants to go out.

He hates going to school,
When he puts up his hair he looks really cool.
No one has a better friend than me,
Don't you see?

Ruairi Mc Garvey (9)
St Brigid's Primary School, Cranagh

MY FAMILY

My family are awfully funny,
Oh and even lovely Mummy.
She rushes around, feet off the ground,
Never making one small sound.
My daddy is a hardworking man,
He works as hard as he can.
My three brothers, they are a pain,
Sometimes I think they are insane!
I am the only girl in our house,
Mummy thinks I'm as quiet as a mouse.
We have a gerbil, his name is Stu',
All he does is chew, chew, chew.
When we take him out,
We must not shout,
For he will run away
And will not stay.
When we go shopping in the big city, Derry,
My family and I are always very merry.
I love my family very much,
We are a cool, trendy bunch!

Laura McAneney (11)
St Brigid's Primary School, Cranagh

MY BEST FRIEND

My best friend's name is Ruairi,
He is a lot of fun,
His favourite toys are tractors
And he plays with them a lot.

When I am down at his house,
I'm welcomed in with joy,
When I am in his bedroom,
The only toys that I can see
Are tractors here and there.

When we are going outside,
We run and get the go-kart,
Then we take it up the path
And ride down to the bottom.

Kieran McAneney (10)
St Brigid's Primary School, Cranagh

MY DOGS

My dog, Glen
Lives in a pen.
He likes to chase the hens.
My friend Jen, doesn't like Glen,
But she's still my best friend.
My other dog, Ben
Drives Jen round the bend.
Once I asked her which one she liked best,
She said, 'I think I like the hens!'

John Campbell (9)
St Brigid's Primary School, Cranagh

MY PET

My pet is really funny,
It hops around like a bunny,
When he comes out,
I just scream and shout.
When my cousin saw him,
She thought he would eat her.
When we clean the cage,
He gets into a mad rage.

Shane McAneney (9)
St Brigid's Primary School, Cranagh

THE TOAD

There was a toad,
That jumped down the road.
It saw a frog on a log in the bog.
The frog saw a dog that saw a cat.
The dog ran after the cat,
The cat ran after a rat.
The rat bumped into an eagle,
That flew after a seagull.
The eagle bumped into a tree,
Beside a monkey that rode a donkey.
They came back to the toad
With a terrible load,
It ate so much, it was dead
And everything went to the toad's funeral.

Ruairi McCusker (9)
St Macartan's Primary School, Dromore

THE SWIMMING POOL

I can float, hooray,
But I've forgotten my gear,
So I can't go in,
But I can still watch.
I just love Wednesdays,
Here's the bus now,
We will be on our way.
There is a fuss on the bus,
Who is the best at swimming.
'Stop your fussing,
We will soon be there and we'll find out!'

Gerard Quinn (9)
St Macartan's Primary School, Dromore

THE SWIMMING POOL

Look, there's the bus! Can we go now?
Skipping and jumping and shouting too,
People are talking and saying, 'Move, move!'
All the children are splashing and diving,
Glad that they're skiving off school for one hour.
But when I am leaving, I look so sour
That I don't even cheer up when I see a lovely flower.

Emma Muldoon (10)
St Macartan's Primary School, Dromore

ROLLER COASTER

Swarm of butterflies,
Spinning round and around,
I'm feeling sick,
My heart stops,
I can't breathe,
I'm scared,
Food churning,
I can't speak,
My eyes are watering,
I can't stand,
Knees are wobbling back and forward,
I've collapsed!

Cathy Monaghan (11)
St Malachy's Primary School, Glencull

SNOW

A white crunch
A powdery spread
A slippery sparkle
A soft ball
A glittery heap
A frozen ground
A silent walk
A sharp-topped icicle.

Kirstie McCreesh (10)
St Malachy's Primary School, Glencull

OCTOPUS

Fun . . . or is it?
My stomach churning
Butterflies fluttering in
My belly . . .
I'm about to be sick!
Thump, thump goes my
Heart in my throat
What am I doing?
My head going round
And round,
My hair standing on end
I want *off!*

Catherine Cassidy (10)
St Malachy's Primary School, Glencull

HUMPTY DUMPTY WENT TO THE MOON

Humpty Dumpty went to the moon
On a supersonic spoon.
He brought porridge and a tent,
But when he got there
The spoon was bent.
Humpty didn't care
And for all I know,
He is still up there!

Loretta Kelly (10)
St Malachy's Primary School, Glencull

FEELING SICK

I'm feeling sick
And terribly weak.
My head is pounding
And I can hardly speak.

My throat is tightening,
It feels raw and dry.
The thought of rising
Makes me want to cry.

I try to surface
From my warm nest,
But my head is spinning,
I need to rest!

I hate this feeling,
It is no fun!
Lying here miserable,
When I should be playing in the sun.

Mum tries to console me,
She does sympathise.
Her words are comforting,
Soothing and wise.

So I'll just lie here
And suffer this quest.
To get better soon
Is my request!

Grainne Harper (10)
St Malachy's Primary School, Glencull

SNOW

A white cover,
A sparkly ground,
A crunchy noise,
A soft fall,
A still surface,
A wavy look,
A fluffy saying,
A slippy surface,
A fun time too.

Eoghan McGirr (10)
St Malachy's Primary School, Glencull

WITCHES

Beware of the witches
Flying about,
Whizzing on broomsticks,
All of them out,
Spells and potions,
Cats and ghosts,
Ugly and black . . .
They're back!

Aidan Quinn (9)
St Malachy's Primary School, Glencull

CAN YOU HEAR?

Can you hear . . .
The whiz of motorbikes?
The zoom of cars?
The whistling of wind?
The thud of feet?
The bang of doors?
The smash of glasses?
The moo of cows?
The mumble of voices?
The chugging of tractors?

Stephen Hackett (11)
St Malachy's Primary School, Glencull

I'D RATHER BE . . .

I'd rather be a hat than a shawl
I'd rather be big than small
I'd rather be tiny than tall
I'd rather be a mirror than a hall
I'd rather be a person than a doll
I'd rather be a nutter than a wall
I'd rather trip than fall
I'd rather have all than the mall!

PJ McKenna (11)
St Malachy's Primary School, Glencull

SOCKS

Socks was my best friend,
Five months old,
Now he's dead,
He was always playing,
He'd bite my wellies,
Shake them,
Hide them,
He'd play bouncy ball,
His special treat was a chocolate biscuit,
I'll always miss him.

Conor McDonald (11)
St Malachy's Primary School, Glencull

CAT

Granda's cat,
Old and fat,
Sat for days
On the mat,
Out came a rat,
It went scat
And that was the
End of that!

Darragh McAnenly (11)
St Malachy's Primary School, Glencull

TIME, FRIENDS, LIFE

Time, what is time?
Is it a whisper of life or a long-term situation?
For far away in a distant land,
Time is ticking for those less fortunate.
But suddenly, time is silenced similar to a statue,
Quiet and motionless.
So for some people, a minute seems like a day
And a day seems like a week.
So take my advice, don't waste time.

Friends are like people who never let you down.
They pick you up when you fall
And think of you as something
That is worth being friends with.
You should never go against your friend
Nor do anything to hurt them.
For when you act in an unreasonable way,
Like not being faithful, or kind,
You wake up one morning
To find that they are gone.

Life is not a simple thing,
It's not like a feather that feels like velvet,
Or a rainbow with vivid colours.
It's very complicated and confusing,
So take the time to think
About the smaller things in life
And you find that, it's an adventure,
That's repeated slowly,
Over and over again.

Bridgeen Campbell (11)
St Mary's Primary School, Pomeroy

IRELAND

32 countries and the grass is really green,
Four provinces, Ulster, Munster, Leinster and Connaught
Hills and valleys, ones the Yanks have never seen,
Ireland welcomes all, even though it's quite small.

Years ago it was cottages being built,
But stacks of flats are being built instead,
On TV there are ads for Lilt,
Instead of fiddlers playing.

Ireland has changed; it's different now,
The population is increasing,
The fields are full of houses instead of cows
And the cities are full of nightclubs.

The weather hasn't changed much, mostly it rains,
But when the sun does come out,
It's still not as hot as Spain
And when the frost comes out, cold seems warm!

Dublin is Ireland's capital city,
Belfast is Northern Ireland's,
Ireland is split in two, what a pity,
We're hoping that will change.

Aisling Mills (11)
St Mary's Primary School, Pomeroy

A WINDY DAY

It was a windy day on the second of May
The park we played in was old and really cold
The children were playing on the cold day of May
There were parades and bands all over the land
When it got dark, everyone left the park
The next day I phoned my friend
The phone call would never end
He told me something interesting
That I had to scream and sing

That day when the parades and bands
Were up and down and all around
There was something wrong
They didn't know the song
That night I had a fight with them
I found out that they were aliens from space
And now in this Irish place
The aliens took over the world
And their favourite pet is a squirrel
They like a cool drink but they don't like the sink
And their favourite colour is pink
We were in a situation
But for the aliens it was vacation
Our lives ended so bad
Everyone was sad.

Barry Quinn (10)
St Mary's Primary School, Stewartstown

THE SNOWSTORM

The snow it came at last
I ran over to the window, fast
There I saw a white land
Where up above
White clouds did fan

We all shouted
'Out to play,
Quickly go and get the sleigh!'

The snowman we did plan
Small head, big body
But never a hand

Next, for a snowball fight
As the north wind
It did bite

Hats, scarves, gloves
We did wear
These frosty conditions
Were hard to bear

Mother said,
'No school, that's sad.'
We all shouted,
'That's too bad!'

Sadly next day
The snow had to go
Where did it go?
I just don't know.

Una McCann (9)
St Mary's Primary School, Stewartstown

MY SPECIAL FRIENDS

I have two very special friends,
I visit them at weekends.

The youngest is called Catarina,
She would like to be a ballerina.

The eldest is called Veronica,
She likes to play the harmonica.

When we play we have great fun,
They really love sitting in the sun.

Their skin is a lovely light brown,
We love going shopping up the town.

They eat lots of healthy food
And never ever be rude.

I learn words in their language,
'Brocha' means 'a witch'.

Veronica's hair is short, curly and black,
She puts in flower clips to tie it back.

Catarina's hair is long and straight,
Sometimes I call her 'Kate'.

They are special because they are Portuguese
And so funny, I fall to my knees.

So that's all I can say about my friends,
That's why I really like weekends!

Hannah Devlin (9)
St Mary's Primary School, Stewartstown

MY POEM

Saddam Hussein, he's insane
He's caused an awful ruction
But Tony Blair, he doesn't care
He's searching for weapons of mass destruction

Now President Bush is in a rush
There isn't time to wait
He wants to go to the Gulf and fight
Because he thinks his army's great

Well old Saddam's a deadly man
And so is his friend, bin Laden
If they don't pull up their socks and behave
No country on Earth will have 'em!

Christopher Coyle (9)
St Mary's Primary School, Stewartstown

A SUMMER'S DAY

One hot summer's day,
We all decided to go away.
As we drove in the car,
I was eating my peach,
As we arrived at the beach.

As I made sandcastles in the sand,
My mummy asked me if I needed a hand.
When I went home I took out my ball
And started to kick it against the wall.

My mummy came out to say,
'Nicola, I think it's time to hit the hay.'
And that was my day!

Nicola Coyle (9)
St Mary's Primary School, Stewartstown

CATNAP CATNIP

Down among the catnip,
By the garden wall,
Cats are sniffing,
Up tails and all.

Black cats, white cats,
Ginger cats and tabby;
Fat cats, slight cats,
The skinny, the flabby.

Long cats, sleek cats,
Tortoiseshell and brindly,
Strong cats, weak cats,
The sturdy and the spindly.

Street cats, fleet cats,
In and out of the shadows;
Tree cats, free cats,
Hunting in the meadows.

Caoimhe Mulgrew (9)
St Mary's Primary School, Stewartstown

FRIENDS FOREVER

You're my friend until the day I die
The day I lose you is the day I'll cry
You're my angel, sent to me
Caught in my he-art until I set you free
Friends forever - you and me.

Naomi Robinson (8)
St Mary's Primary School, Stewartstown

TYRONE VS GALWAY

Tryone played Galway in Pomeroy today
The fans from Galway had come a long way
Tyrone had taken an early lead from the start
The Tribesmen from Galway seemed to lose heart

I watched the game from the stand
If I was needed I would lend a hand
But Brian Dooher himself did hammer the net
I stayed where I was, excited but wet

The game ended, the roar went up
I thought we had won the cup
Dad said, 'Put the celebrations on hold,
It's a long way to September and All Ireland Gold!'

Christopher McNally (9)
St Mary's Primary School, Stewartstown

HOLIDAY TIME

H appy families play in the sun,
O pen space for the children to roam and play free,
'L ife on holiday is worth living for!' everyone shouted
I magination comes alive, as we all can see.
D ays and weeks pass as we swim and have fun.
A t times it's tiring and boring too.
Y awn as everyone is tired and goes to bed.
S ummertime holidays are waiting for you!

Laura Tierney (8)
St Mary's Primary School, Stewartstown

THE FAMINE

Heartbreaking
Distressing
Worried and
Nervous.

I'm cold and I'm weak, I just can't go on
I'm worried and I'm downhearted
Because my family have gone
It took their souls and it's coming for mine
I suffer and cry, I'm tired and lonely.

Heartbreaking
Distressing
Worried and
Nervous.

Pale faces stare, an odour spreads
Lots of worry lines, you can see in their heads
Pain rises through everyone's body
This is only torture but when will it end?

People have changed from wealthy to weak
Dead bodies are everywhere
Through hills and towns I see people weep
I'm poor with no money but nobody cares.

Everybody's the same
Oh, when will this end?
I long to be in Heaven with my family and friends.

Natalie McKay (11)
St Patrick's Primary School, Castlederg

HUNGER!

The heartbreaking sorrow on every exhausted face
The suffering of the feeble bodies
The worry in everyone's minds
The hunger, oh the hunger!

The black forty-seven, more disaster and death
The pain and suffering soaking through every soul
The torture and the fear
The hunger, oh the hunger!

Downhearted cries and the wailing goes on
Not a penny to be given, not a smile to be smiled
The misery reigning and the spirit dying
The hunger, oh the hunger!

Walking phantoms roaming the streets
Isolated and lonely
The crying not able to go on
The hunger, oh the hunger!

Pity dwells and hopelessness bites upon the white
Anxious flesh
The cold, dark surroundings
The hunger, oh the hunger!

The 1850s, thank God it has passed
Millions are lost now
Millions have gone.

Seanain McGuigan (11)
St Patrick's Primary School, Castlederg

DREAM

Curling
Floating
Whirling
Floating everywhere
Different colours.
I am sailing along
I am sliding along to a
Deep dark colour.
I feel relaxed, exhausted
I want to go to sleep.
It is colourful, I can't stop sliding
It is too good to sleep on.
I can see the red and pink blending
In with the silver and gold.

Maureen Bogle (10)
St Patrick's Primary School, Castlederg

DREAM

Spinning, swirling, twisting, flying through the air,
Different colours everywhere,
Pink, blue, green, yellow, silver and purple too.
Circles, triangles, squares, rectangles, lots of shapes and sizes.
Sliding, dizzy, powerful, rough, I'm travelling at top speed.
Dazzled, upset, dazed, confused, bewildered, jumbled.
What has just happened?
Lots of milkshakes, banana, strawberry, chocolate,
Chocolate truffles, Turkish Delights, Dairy Milk.

I'm in Heaven!

Colette Corry (10)
St Patrick's Primary School, Castlederg

THE FAMINE

Hardship and torment
And despair in your heart
You're anxious and you're worried
You're falling apart
You're feeble and weak
And simply can't go on
You're feeling alone and resentful
Your family have already gone

Hunger and misery
Your heart is full of fear
You're tired and exhausted
That's the landlord you can hear
He'll throw you out of your house
Unless the rent you pay
You may have managed this one
But he'll be back another day

When you enter the workhouse
A horrible stench greets you
There are dead people around you
You think, *I'm going to die in here too.*
Pain and anguish and worry
Come whatever may
You're 100% certain
You'll never escape from here any day . . .

Edel Byrne (10)
St Patrick's Primary School, Castlederg

WINTER

Winter has a split personality, sometimes
It is miserable, bare and wet
The scenery is bitter, dull and grey
Like a grey cloud covering everything
It's like a dismal, dark hole

It's sometimes like a depressed
Gloomy, isolated hill
Winter can be very miserable
And tormenting

But sometimes winter can be
Beautiful and joyful
When you're playing about in the
Wonderful white snow that falls
Softly onto the ground

Winter can be more fun than
Anything for children
Throwing snowballs and rolling
In the snow
The glint and shine of winter is precious
So we should cherish it.

Conaill Carolan (11)
St Patrick's Primary School, Castlederg

HALLOWE'EN

On Hallowe'en Night
When the sky is dark
When the ravens fly over the treetops
Quietly, this is what you would hear:

A laugh from a fairy
Dainty and small
A grunt from an ugly old gnome
And a squeak from a cute little pixie.

On Hallowe'en Night
When the werewolves
Howl at the moon
This is what you would see:

The smoke from the witch's potion
All bubbly and green
The shadow cast by a bogeyman
The gleam from the red-eyed monster.

On Hallowe'en Night
When the fog is thick
And there's not a star to be seen
This is what you would feel:

The chill down your spine
Sent by the grey old wizard
The nip from the bloodthirsty vampire on your neck
And the cold, bony finger on your shoulder.

On Hallowe'en Night
When the wind
Echoes through the woods
This is what you would smell:

The stench of the flesh
Of a decayed zombie
The choking steam of the fires of Hell
The poisonous scent of the witch's brew.

On Hallowe'en Night
When the lightning strikes
And the ghouls are all about
This is what they do:

The witch makes a gooey cake
The bogeyman's brothers play in a band
And all the spooks run wild!

'How do I know this?'
Is that what you ask?
Well, this is the answer I have to tell
I was there, in the flesh
Watching the ghouls at their party bash
I have seen what no other being has seen
I have seen the creeps of Hallowe'en!

Patrick McAnea (9)
St Patrick's Primary School, Castlederg

FEAR!

Fear is when you're falling and falling and can't stop,
You're stuck,
You can't move,
You can't see anything but black, pure black fear.

Fear is when your heart is pumping, your breath is heavy,
You're falling and falling and can't stop,
You're stuck, you can't move,
You can't see anything but black, pure black fear.

Fear is when you're isolated, you're paralysed,
You can do nothing but let it take over,
You're falling and falling and you can't stop,
You're stuck,
You can't see anything but black,
Pure black fear taking over and covering your body,
Smothering you till you just give up.

That's what fear is.

Niall Lynch (11)
St Patrick's Primary School, Castlederg

WINTER WEATHER

Winter is the coldness in the air and the wind torturing the bare trees,
Winter is the soft snow falling on the ground,
Winter is the gloomy, dark, dull nights that I can't go out to play,
Winter is children playing happily on the ice,
Winter is the eerie, foggy nights coming, descending upon us,

Winter is children building snowmen, bigger and better every time,
Winter is walking home from school in the bitter days without a coat,
Winter is sitting up in front of a fire sipping a cup of hot chocolate,
Winter is the snow landing on your sleeve then melting
And that is what I think winter means to me.

Grainne McGirr (11)
St Patrick's Primary School, Castlederg

EVERYBODY, EVERYONE

Everybody, everyone,
In the play yard having fun.
Everybody, everyone,
In the assembly hall not having much fun.
Until the principal gives out the awards,
To the people who deserve them most.
Everybody, everyone,
In the classroom learning,
Learning some maths, some English too,
Learning some maths, some poetry too.

Everybody, everyone,
Come along and join the fun.
Everybody, everyone,
Don't be studying, have some fun,
One and one,
Just have some fun,
One and two,
I'm glad I'm not you.
Everybody, everyone,
Come along and join the fun!

Emma Clements (9)
St Patrick's Primary School, Dungannon

MY SNOW POEM

Snow comes down from the sky,
Let's play,
You and I,
Make a snowman,
Have some fun,
Don't you worry,
The day has just begun,
Time for tea . . .
'Grandma won't you come out?'
'I can't, little dear,
I have a fear
Of me slipping.'
'Where's my dad?'
'I don't know.'
'The phone's ringing, Gran.'
'That must be Dan.'
'No it isn't,
It's Dad,
He is stuck on the snow!'

Shannon Lafferty (8)
St Patrick's Primary School, Dungannon

THE WEATHER

The weather makes me cold
The weather makes me stay in all day long
The weather makes me wet
The weather makes me warm
The weather makes me shiver
The weather makes me smile.

Kelly Mallon (7)
St Patrick's Primary School, Dungannon

MY CHESTNUT TREE

One night long ago
Queen of the fairies planted a tree
For fairies to dance under in two thousand and three
At night when humans are asleep
The head fairy takes a peep
If it is clear, the fairies start dancing
And above them the tree is prancing
From its mangled roots, fall blossomed flowers
Onto their silky, golden hair it showers
It sets an illusion in the daylight
So people don't see them and get a fright
One winter night the snow was so thick
The clock went tick, tick
Soon it was morning and Lauren looked outside
She saw the fairies and the fairies saw her
What could she do but stare?
The fairies disappeared and so did the tree
And from that moment on the fairies danced at a different tree.

Lauren Watson (9)
St Patrick's Primary School, Dungannon

HALLOWE'EN NIGHT

It's Hallowe'en night and the witches come out tonight
To be honest, it gives me quite a fright
The ghosts and ghouls come out to play
I wish they came out another day
But no, it's only superstition
I don't believe it
But - do you?

Catherine Winters (8)
St Patrick's Primary School, Dungannon

SCHOOL

When you go to school you take a rubber and a pencil with you,
it helps you with everything you want to do.

Dinner time is my time for eating
and I always hear the little birds tweeting.

The playground is perfect for playing every game
and all my friends like doing the very same.

Home time makes me really *mad*,
because going home makes me sad.

I work all day, then it's time to rest,
can't wait to do PE, it's the best.

Sorcha Dinsmore (8)
St Patrick's Primary School, Dungannon

MY BROTHER

I have a brother who is really funny,
He's got ears shaped like a bunny.
He always jumps a lot,
Every time his ears go pop.
He is handsome, he is smart,
He can make a very nice apple tart.
I like him
And his toenails are shaped like a shark's fin.
He likes me,
If I pay him a small fee.
His first name begins with T,
Who is he?
Yes, that's right, he is Timothy.

James Murphy (8)
St Patrick's Primary School, Dungannon

A POEM ABOUT MY PET DOG

My dog's called Tiny
because she's so small.

She has a cute face and scruffy fur.

When I go to school
she looks so sad.

When I come home
she's so glad.

She runs around my feet
and wags her tail.

I can see the love in her face.

I love her.

Rebecca Hand (8)
St Patrick's Primary School, Dungannon

AUTUMN

In autumn the trees don't have enough energy
To keep their leaves,
They gently fall to the ground.
They change colour to gold, rust and brown.
The weather is cold and windy.
The leaves blow away in the air.
You can feel a nip in the air.
Our feet crunch the leaves as we run.
You can hear them rustling.

Conor McNeill (8)
St Patrick's Primary School, Dungannon

MY BABY SISTER

She smiles, she cries,
She says *goo-goo*.
She looks at me,
She looks at you.
She moves her arms,
She kicks her legs.
She sucks her dummy
As she lies in bed.
She's small, she's fun,
When I'm at school, I miss her,
She is Michaela, my baby sister.
Now she is one!
She's starting to walk,
She's sleeping all night
And learning to talk.
She plays with her toys,
She eats up her food -
All in all, she's ever so good.
Although she's a baby,
I can't wait to see
What she will be like
When she's the same age as me.

Marianne McCann (9)
St Patrick's Primary School, Dungannon

MOLE

M aking mischief under the ground.
O ften doing it without a sound.
L aughing and giggling is what they like to do.
E nding the day by making a mound.

Rory McCooey (8)
St Patrick's Primary School, Dungannon

WONDAQUE!

Wondaque walked through monster land,
He spotted a monster harming man,
He grabbed the monster with his chain hand,
His eyes burnt the monster like a frying pan.

'Wondaque has saved the day again,
With his super long chain hands,
We don't think he's insane,
Here in the monster lands!'

Wondaque went up into the tower,
Old King Cole was trying to steal,
Wondaque was full of power
And ate him for his meal.

'Wondaque has saved the day again,
With his super long chain hands,
We don't think he's insane,
Here in the monster lands!'

Sarah Loughran (9)
St Patrick's Primary School, Dungannon

SCHOOL

School is where we learn lots of things,
there is maths and English and we even sing.

Our classroom is bright and full of colour,
there's yellow and blue and many others.

The classroom is sometimes quiet,
because children are working hard,
even though there is plenty of noise,
coming from the yard.

Rebecca McGuigan (7)
St Patrick's Primary School, Dungannon

My Extraordinary Cat

My cat is very clever, he is one in a million,
Instead of acting like a cat, he acts more like a son.
When he gets sleepy, he does not curl up in a ball,
Instead he stretches himself flat out in the hall.

When I go on holiday, he misses me so much,
But when I come back home again, he loves my gentle touch.
One time we went on holiday and left my cat at home
And when we came back home again, the house was on its own.

For days and days we waited, feeling sad and alone,
But then one day he reappeared and joy fulfilled our home.
Late one night we all decided to go for a walk
And very soon he suddenly walked up to hear our talk.

My cat's truly amazing, the finest in the land,
Instead of eating from a bowl, he eats out of my hand.
He is the sweetest little pet; I call him my wee honey,
He does so many clever things and acts so very funny.

Rachel Kane (11)
St Patrick's Primary School, Dungannon

World War II

Hitler led Germany in World War II
He fought American, England, France and Russia too
People had to evacuate
Men had to go and fight
The government told them to
Eat less, save, not spend
England and its allies won in the end.

Oisin Shields (7)
St Patrick's Primary School, Dungannon

FOURTEEN HEADS

Fourteen heads and twenty-four toes,
Where he lives, no one knows,
Late at night in snow and sleet,
Around the rubbish skips he creeps.

Any old clothes or bits of rubble,
He'll take everything without any trouble,
Sticks and stones or coloured beads,
Bags and bags of rotting leaves.

Some people say he carries a spear
And guzzles down a bucket of beer,
No one seems to really care
About the flames in his hair.

Be careful what you throw out,
You never know when he's about,
Poking through our rubbish skips,
Smiling with fourteen pairs of lips.

Sean Hughes (9)
St Patrick's Primary School, Dungannon

MATHS

M aths is fun, we get so much done,
A dding and taking away are things we learn,
T ables and sums are so much fun.
H aving counters can do so much,
S howing all different ways to count is a special touch.

Kyna Dinsmore (7)
St Patrick's Primary School, Dungannon

GRANDMA

I know someone who is very smart,
She has children 4 years apart.
She was there at World War II,
She did not know what to do.
She is very, very kind
And of course, has a good mind.
She is sometimes very funny
And quite often she gives us money.
So now you guess who she is,
This will get you in a tiz.
Here's a clue, she is nearly Nana,
Who is she? Yes! She is my grandma.

Andrew Murphy (8)
St Patrick's Primary School, Dungannon

GRANNY'S KITCHEN

In Granny's kitchen there are lots of things,
Granny works while the telephone rings.
I help cook the food,
It really is quite good.
We always get a biscuit or sweet
And Granny then gets us out from under her feet.
From Granny's kitchen, there's a wonderful view,
Every time I look out, there is something new.
I love my granny and she loves me.

Sarah Canavan (8)
St Patrick's Primary School, Dungannon

COMPUTERS

As I switch on the computer
The screen begins to glow
With a flash something comes up
It's time for me to log on
When I type in my name and password
A blue screen appears
I click on start to open the menu
A new world opens up
A world of fun where you can play games
Write stories, download pictures
Learn about WWII
Or go on the Internet
Or just have fun!

Daniel Maguire (8)
St Patrick's Primary School, Dungannon

OH SCHOOL IS JUST OK

Just another day at school,
reading, writing and doing sums.
Looking forward to break time,
so I can get some play time.
Back in the classroom once more,
so we can learn a little more.
Watching the clock until it's home time.
Please teacher, let us play a little more!

Dermott Burns (8)
St Patrick's Primary School, Dungannon

HOMEWORK

Homework, what a bother
Especially on my mother
English, history and maths
All of these different paths.

Homework, homework, it *stinks!*
I wish I could wash you down the sink.

Homework, it's the last on my list
If only I could smash you with my fist
Then my time would be free
To go out and play, would you agree?

Gareth Cullen (7)
St Patrick's Primary School, Dungannon

MY WATCH

I have a watch; it is very small,
I sometimes hang it on my wall.
When morning comes, it gives a bleep,
It wakens me from my sleep.
The strap is black, the face is white,
It sometimes frightens me at night.
I love this little watch of mine,
Gran brought it for me at Christmas time.
I'll keep it safe, close to my heart
And it and I will never part!

Arthur Rafferty (7)
St Patrick's Primary School, Dungannon

MY FAVOURITE FRIEND

My favourite friend is
As kind as a really good friend,
As shy as a dormouse,
As strong as strong glass,
He laughs when Conor makes a joke,
Messes about sometimes,
A good friend to everyone,
Good writing all the time,
He has only got in trouble once or twice,
Good at games
And he is smart.

David Mills
St Patrick's Primary School, Dungannon

FROSTY DAY

The world looks frosty, white and sparkling,
Gleaming, dazzling, shining,
People ice-skate gracefully,
Sliding, gliding, glowing,
Children build a bulgy snowman,
Giggling, laughing, cheering,
Decorate him with a colourful hat and scarf,
Throwing, dancing, fixing,
Robins chirping and searching for food,
Whistling, singing, hunting.

Conor McNally (9)
St Patrick's Primary School, Dungannon

THE SNOW!

Feather snowflakes coming down on my head,
Twirling, swirling, drifting.

Icy cold night and trees are dead,
Shifting, swerving, dripping.

Everyone is doing their little do,
Riding, sliding, skipping.

Around the snowman there's a hullabaloo,
Riding, sliding, skipping.

They built a wonderful snowman,
Riding, sliding, skipping.

Winter's nearly over and snow turns to slush,
Twirling, swirling, drifting.

The fun is over and no more snow,
Melting, slushing, disappearing.

Niall Kelly (8)
St Patrick's Primary School, Dungannon

CHILDHOOD

Childhood is as baby-blue as the great sky,
It smells of a dainty bouquet of white roses,
It tastes like freshly-squeezed oranges,
Childhood sounds like merry children playing in the snowy streets,
It feels like a fluffy cat's fur,
Childhood lives in the depths of a small child's heart.

Laura Deery (11)
St Patrick's Primary School, Dungannon

MY GREAT GRAN

I once had a great-gran
And she was my number one fan,
She showed me how to knit
And beside her, I would sit.

She had a dog named Patch
And every night he kept watch,
He enjoyed his daily bone
And kept a listen for the phone.

Every day she would bake
Bread, buns and a cake,
Tasty fish in the pan,
That's why I love my great-gran!

Eimear Casey (9)
St Patrick's Primary School, Dungannon

WHAT IF . . .

If I were a dolphin
I could play among the reefs all day
I could search for treasure
I would glisten in the sunlight
And jump in the air
I would splash all night and day
I would jump through hoops
I would jump off waterfalls
I would play with my dolphin friends
If only I were a dolphin . . .

Meghan McCaul (9)
St Patrick's Primary School, Dungannon

WATCH OUT

In a forest far away,
The twister sweeps around,
Following a trail that leads him astray,
To a body on the ground.

With eyes that kill with just one glance,
Massive hands that crush to bits,
The twister does a wicked dance,
Scaring little kids out of their wits.

People chase the twister,
Day and night,
But when they catch it,
It's treacherous as they have
To put up a fight.

With eyes that kill with just one glance,
Massive hands that crush to bits,
The twister does a wicked dance,
Scaring little kids out of their wits.

Anna Deery (8)
St Patrick's Primary School, Dungannon

IF . . .

If I was a cheetah how fast I would run
I'd hunt all night and then lie in the sun
I'd live in the jungle and let out a roar
And think of my dinner, a fat, juicy boar

I'd be my own boss and not have any rules
I wouldn't have to go to any old schools
My fur it is spotty and shiny and warm
It keeps me dry in all kinds of storm

My teeth they are sharp and would bite you in half
You'd better start running, no time to laugh
If I catch you at all, it will be too late
You will end up, no doubt, on my dinner plate

I hunt all the time and don't need much rest
I'm agile and fast and simply the best
If I was a cheetah where would *you* be?
If you are wise you'd be hiding from me.

Shae McKernan (9)
St Patrick's Primary School, Dungannon

MY COUSIN, SHEA

My cousin, Shea
Lives up in Ballynahaye.
He has a very big smile
But when he is in a bad mood, it lasts just a while,

He loves playing in the muck,
With all his cars and trucks.
He watches TV
And loves sitting upon Grandad's knee.

He is in Primary One
And when school's over, he loves to run and run.
Homework is not his favourite thing to do,
But when he is big like me, he'll love it too.

Sometimes Shea and I fight,
But when he stays, he loves cuddling up at night.
Most of the time Shea is good,
But he is my cousin and I love him in any mood.

Cara Donnelly (9)
St Patrick's Primary School, Dungannon

MY DOG, ZAC

My dog, Zac has big brown eyes
And floppy ears, his coat is jet-black.

He lives outside in his own little house,
in our garden out the back.

I love my dog so very much
and I know that he loves me 'cause
when I go out to see him
he jumps all over me.

Naomi Campbell (8)
St Patrick's Primary School, Dungannon

SNOW

Snow is fun
You can make things like snowmen and snow angels
I like snowball fights
When I get cold I come in
It feels like my toes are going to fall off
My fingers feel like they have already.

Andrew Watson (8)
St Patrick's Primary School, Dungannon

WITCHES

I was sitting in the house
When the lights went out
I think there must be a witch about
Is she under the table?
Behind the chair
Or is she hiding under the stairs?

I think there must be a witch about
Is she under my bed
Or just in my head?
I think there *must* be a witch about!

Aimee-Lee Kinnear (8)
St Patrick's Primary School, Dungannon

WALKING IN THE WINTER WONDERLAND

Children playing in the snow,
Having lots of fun,
Jack Frost drawing everywhere,
Leaving lots of ice sculptures,
Teeth are chattering all day long,
Feeling extremely cold,
Snowflakes falling from the sky,
Everywhere is white.

Marian Barker (9)
St Patrick's Primary School, Dungannon

MY GRAN

My gran is as good as gold
Her hair is like wire
Her eyes are like the stars
Her face is like snow
When she walks she is like a penguin
When she sits she is like a bird on a branch
When she laughs she is like a hyena
When she sleeps she is like a baby
The best thing about my gran is she loves me.

David McManus (9)
St Patrick's Primary School, Dungannon

THE SEA

The sea is something gentle,
The sea is sometimes rough,
The sea can be cruel and
The sea will get back at you.
With its huge, crashing waves it will blow your boat away
And with its enormous storms whirling
Around the lighthouse all day,
All the sailors can see the warning
Of the lighthouse that shines brightly every night.
But in the morning, when the storms are away
And the sun is shining bright and the sea is calm and still,
People ready to play, but beware -
Maybe the sea has something to say.

Gerard Currie (9)
St Patrick's Primary School, Dungannon

WHAT IF . . .

If I were a snake, slithering along the ground.
I could play among the treetops and hang upside down.
I could squeeze the tree trunks
And bite you with my poisonous bite,
Which would really show my spite.
All the animals would make way
For the rest of the day.
I could slither through the root of a tree
And lay my eggs where no one could see.
If only I were a snake for the day
And snooze on the jungle bay.

Ryan Devlin (9)
St Patrick's Primary School, Dungannon

THE KILLER

One morning
When I was going to school
I heard a scream
It seemed to be
Coming from the drain
I looked
Down and . . .
I saw . . .
A big, scary monster
And then it got . . .
Meee!

Lorchan Ritchie (9)
St Patrick's Primary School, Dungannon

SUMMER SET BAY

If I were a dolphin
I would ride through the waves
I would journey from coast to coast, making friends on the way!
All the crabs and seashells would wave and laugh with glee
When they'd see me riding and gliding through the sea
I'd make my home among the coral reefs beside Summer Set Bay.
I would play all night and play all day, oh how I love fun and play!
But when the night comes, I would stop all play,
I'd settle down to bed to save my energy for the next day.
If only I were a dolphin for a day, I would sleep on Summer Set Bay.

Helen Kerr (9)
St Patrick's Primary School, Dungannon

WHAT IF ...

If I were a dolphin I would swim and play with
Fungi in the water, it would be fun.

Fungi lives in Dingle Bay, I go down and visit him,
I could play games with him.

I could jump through hoops all through the day
And I could sleep from morning till night.

If I were a dolphin for just a day, it would be fun.

Kerrie-Ann Kelly (8)
St Patrick's Primary School, Dungannon

MY FAMILY!

In my family there is me, Mum and Dad
And of course my sisters who are not really bad.
Sometimes we have lots of fun,
In the summer we play in the sun.

One day we were jumping on the beds,
Patricia and me, we bumped our heads,
My head was really sore all night,
But in the morning, it was alright.

Michaela gets spoilt every day,
She always gets her own way,
Michaela is not small,
So that's my family and I love them all.

Catherine Morris (10)
St Peter's Primary School, Plumbridge

SCHOOL TIME

School is just OK I think
Sometimes it can really stink
Sometimes schoolwork can be a bore
But as for homework, what a chore
Night after night
I write and write
And the teacher marks it in daylight
And says you really aren't that bright
Teachers are a real pest
I think home is the best
But when it's all said and done
St Peter's School is number one!

Seamus Maloney (10)
St Peter's Primary School, Plumbridge

CHOCOLATE FACTORY

I wish I had a chocolate factory
I'd live in it if I could
I would have a tree of lollipops
And a garden with drinks of all kinds
Sweets would be popping up everywhere
The one thing I would want best is a chocolate river
With a boat to go through it
I would invite all my friends
I would have a room for all my inventions -
I'd make a sweet that would never lose its taste.

Christina McAneney (10)
St Peter's Primary School, Plumbridge

I Don't Want To

'I don't want to eat my food!
And no, I'm not in a bad mood!
I don't want to take a bath!
And no, don't think you can laugh!

I want my dessert, I want it here!
Quick, I feel a tantrum coming near
I'm not going to bed! What!
You heard what I said!
'Cause you can't make me, I don't want to!

Come on! Come on! Come on!
No! *You* go to *your* bed, *you* go and eat *your* food!
You get *your* dessert and *you* go and take a bath! *You!*
There are poor and hungry children in this lonely little world,
You are very lucky you have everything,
Now get ready and go to bed.'

That night I thought about my strange mood swings,
Then in my head a little bell rings,
Hey, for poor people, we can do lots of things,
That night I lay on my bed dreaming of space,
School, TV and all my friends.

Ciara Furey (10)
St Peter's Primary School, Plumbridge

The Attic

Every summer that unpleasant job
Of tidying the attic up.
My friend came,
But when he heard of the job,
He was nowhere to be seen.

My brother climbed the ladder
And he fell,
He ended up in the Mater.
His friend asked where he was,
I told the story and said not to tell.

Joseph Murray (10)
St Peter's Primary School, Plumbridge

MY INVISIBLE FRIEND

I have an invisible friend called Jim
He usually makes an awful din
We go to the park every day
As we always want to play
We might play chess all day long
Or sometimes sit and sing a song
Many times we run on the streets
Before heading home to get some sweets.

Philip Mc Bride (9)
St Peter's Primary School, Plumbridge

LIONS

Lions like to eat meat
And any other animal that gets in their way
And if they cannot find any wild animals,
They would kill goats and cows.
The male lions are very lazy,
Lions like to eat meat,
From head to feet.
They like to eat,
Never leaving any meat.

Ciaran McNulty (9)
St Peter's Primary School, Plumbridge

PARENTS

Parents are two people who look after you
And watch everything you do,
Parents are always really nice,
They're there to help you and give you advice.

Parents, some people have one
And some people have two,
It doesn't matter how many you have, it's always fun,
How many have you?

Parents choose your name at birth,
They always thinks of you first,
Your parents hardly ever get mad,
Unless you've been really bad.

Parents are always there for you,
Believing in everything you do,
Parents are always kind and good,
Unless they're in a bad mood!

Amanda Hood (10)
St Peter's Primary School, Plumbridge

VIKINGS

Vikings had such long beards,
They were kings of the sea.
They had swords and armour which had glamour,
They had boats and they wore coats.
They went to places to fight,
When it was night, they had a light
And when it was morning, they had to go hunting.
When it was dinner time, they went to sea,
To kill a shark to eat.

Leon McNamee (9)
St Peter's Primary School, Plumbridge

SPACE

We live in a galaxy called the Milky Way,
If I could, I'd stare at it all day.
My favourite planet is Mars of course,
But I like planets from a different source.

The sun is in the middle of space,
Keeps everybody warm in the human race.
The moon gives us lots of light,
Especially in the middle of the night.

Pluto is the smallest
And is also the coldest.
Planets are all shapes and sizes in many ways,
The moon goes round the Earth in one day.

Melissa McCullagh (11)
St Peter's Primary School, Plumbridge

CHESS

Chess is the best,
It always beats the rest,
If you try it out,
You will always shout,
It is the best,
Best of the best,
It beats the rest.

Kings, queens and rooks
Are in the books,
All but pawns play on lawns,
They are all important to the game,
Just the same.

Niall Murphy (9)
St Peter's Primary School, Plumbridge

FOOTBALL

Football is my favourite game,
I like to play it,
It gives me some energy,
Football is the best.

Tyrone is my favourite team,
Peter Canavan is the best,
I like him lots,
He is above the rest.

I can solo a ball with my feet,
I can fist a ball with my hand,
I play for Glenelly,
Who are the best team in the land!

Rosaleen Bradley (10)
St Peter's Primary School, Plumbridge

FEARS

Hide under the quilt
Stay still as a statue
Someone is at the window
Don't look now, hide somehow
I think they will go away
Oh, it's coming down the hall
It banged into the wall
The handle on the bedroom door is shaking . . .
The door is opening . . .
Oh no, it is my mum!

Mark Mc Dermott (9)
St Peter's Primary School, Plumbridge

POOR OLD GRANDMA

My old grandma
So many times she's got in a tizzy
I stand and stare
As her hair sticks up all frizzy

Her teeth have all fallen out
And she is bent over like a spout
She sits on the mat
With the cat on her lap

Now I'm older
I don't think she's mad
But I don't understand
Poor old Grandma!

Eva Hicks (9)
St Peter's Primary School, Plumbridge

THE GHOSTS

In a forest there were two ghosts,
They would boast and boast,
They would eat tea and toast.
They come out at night,
They want to give you a fright,
What a scary sight,
'Are you . . . alright?'

Patrick McCrory (10)
St Peter's Primary School, Plumbridge

MY PET

I have a pet,
Once it had to go to the vet.
It got run over on the road,
As it ate a toad.

When it died, I was very sad,
I got really mad,
We buried it in the bog,
I sat all day on a log.

When it died,
I got a new pet,
But this one didn't
Go to the vet . . .

And it didn't die either!

Clodagh Donaghy (9)
St Teresa's Primary School, Loughmacrory

MY DAD'S LORRY

My dad's lorry is very big,
It is a rig,
Shining blue,
With many wheels,
He drives all over the place,
He lets me help him
Load the diggers and things,
'Be careful, don't stand so close
Or you will get hurt.'
'Thanks, Dad!'

Sean Gallagher (8)
St Teresa's Primary School, Loughmacrory

IT'S NOT A DREAM!

It's not a dream!
When he was young
He played on a hurling team!
As he gets older
Lying there,
He's even colder.

It's not a dream!
When I went to see him,
The world was so keen!
Now he's not here,
I even have fear!
But I miss my great uncle Patsy!

Emily Donaghy (10)
St Teresa's Primary School, Loughmacrory

FOOTBALL MAD

When football starts
I be glad
I laugh and cheer
And shout, 'My lad!'

My dad likes to have
A pint of beer
But when we score
He kicks me on the ear

My ears get sore
But I take the beer
I put it down the bathroom sink
And it soon will disappear!

Ryan O'Brien (10)
St Teresa's Primary School, Loughmacrory

SUMMER

On a warm summer's night
While the sky is still bright,
We'll have barbecues with food,
Friends and family, all in a great mood.

A day at the beach,
The sky is pink, red, lilac and peach,
As I run through the sand, I feel the breeze in my hair,
While the salty smell of the sea sticks in the air.

I walk past a rock pool,
The water's quite cool,
I walk with slow steps and a net in my hand,
At the bottom of the pool I see sand.

At home in the sun,
Around the garden I run and run.
I hear the music of the ice cream van
And down I run as fast as I can.

All the creatures of the sea,
All as happy as can be.
At the sea, I wear my swimming suit,
All our belongings packed in the car boot.

We go on our holidays on a plane,
Or a bus, car, boat, maybe a train.
We'll have loads of memories and photos too
And when we look back at them, we'll have fun, me and you.

Now the holidays have ended,
All scraped knees and bandaged arms have mended,
But I'm not sad,
Because I can't wait to tell my friends about the fun I've had.

I think summer's great
Don't you mate?

Aoife Mc Elduff (10)
St Teresa's Primary School, Loughmacrory

THE THINGS I HATE,
THE THINGS THAT ARE GREAT!

The things I hate are maths
And spiders in our baths,
I hate the way we do work every day,
I hardly ever get to play.

The things that I think are great
Are horses and ponies,
They're not phonies,
I draw them on the windows,
In the car.

I hate maths
And spiders in our baths,
I think horses and ponies are great
Because they're not phonies.

Marie Conway (10)
St Teresa's Primary School, Loughmacrory

MY FRIENDS!

My friends are funny,
We love spending money.
Sometimes we tell jokes,
The three of us play together.

We love netball!
One picks the game,
We hate football!
All of us have each other in a photo frame!

We love swimming,
Netball too!
But there's one thing
We all hate, football!

But there's nothing
That will come between us,
Because of our
Relationship!

Meadhbh O'Goan (10)
St Teresa's Primary School, Loughmacrory

PETER'S LORRY

Peter's lorry is blue and white,
He drives along the road on long journeys.

In the middle of the night,
He sleeps in the cab.

I got a ride in it one day,
Peter's lorry is groovy.

Martin McAleer (9)
St Teresa's Primary School, Loughmacrory

CARS

Cars are cool,
Cars are great!
Get a speedy one
And you won't be late.

Cars are speedy,
Cars are shiny,
There are cars that are big,
Cars that are tiny.

Cars that are shiny,
Like a new shiny Ford,
Get in the car
And you won't be bored.

Cars are cool,
Cars are great,
Get a friend
And drive it with your mate.

Connor Grimes (8)
St Teresa's Primary School, Loughmacrory

MY BIG BROTHER

My big brother is called Aidan
He is 12 years of age
Sometimes he tries to hurt me
He is kind to me every day
He lets me play the PlayStation
He always stands up for me
My big brother.

Orla McCullagh (9)
St Teresa's Primary School, Loughmacrory

THE DARK, DARK SEA

The sea is murky and full of gloom,
The worst place is the underwater tomb.

The sharks might get you
And probably say *boo!*

The evil underwater witch
Will trick you and take you to her underwater lair.

The guards will ignore you,
As if you weren't there.

They'll keep you in cages
And when you escape, all you can hear are terrible rages.

The mermaids are down there,
They are the ones who care.

The workers are working,
It's a miracle if you get away with lurking.

They are put in a line
And everything is in a great shine.

They have lovely coral reef flowers
And a lot of powerful showers.

The sea is murky and blue
And some things are as sticky as glue!

Ryan Donaghy (9)
St Teresa's Primary School, Loughmacrory

FOOTY

Footy is good
Footy is great
You could play it with anyone
You could play with a mate

Footy is class
Footy is brill
Oh, would you look at that
It's eleven-nil!

Rory Donaghy (8)
St Teresa's Primary School, Loughmacrory

I MISS YOU, GRANDA

They say the pattering of the rain,
Will heal the memory and heal the pain,
Granda why did you have to go?
Because ever since, we feel so low.

Every since lightning struck,
The day you died,
My whole family
Cried and cried.

My mother was in great pain,
My father cried out in the rain.
They both said, 'Father, why did you go?
Because we miss you so.'

That night I couldn't sleep,
I went downstairs to have a peep
And in the coffin, stiff and cold,
Lay a story that was never told.

A man as stiff as a post,
Much more paler than a ghost,
Then a thought filled my head,
I didn't understand why he was dead.

Granda, why did you have to go
Because we miss you so.

Maire Gallagher (10)
St Teresa's Primary School, Loughmacrory

MY BABY BROTHER

My baby brother is called Shea
And he likes to play
Every single day

My brother eats his food
And he is so good
Sometimes he is in a mood

He likes his mummy
He is so funny
And he has a bunny.

Laura Conway (9)
St Teresa's Primary School, Loughmacrory

IRELAND

Ireland is the world's side of green
It's the best place I've ever seen
In the World Cup we were great
But we were beat

Leprechauns are supposed to be extinct
But I have a little leprechaun friend
He is as sharp as wire
Sometimes he says,
'Go on lady, light a fire!'

Conall Daly (9)
St Teresa's Primary School, Loughmacrory

POP IDOL

Top news, Will and Gareth are in the final
They are trying to do their best
Gareth puts a lot of gel on
Will is getting ready
Gareth dressed like Elvis

They went out on stage
And sang so good
At the end, Ant and Dec said, 'Who has won?'
They said, 'Will!'

He had won
He sang again
Gareth went home happy
That was the end of it.

Laura Rafferty (9)
St Teresa's Primary School, Loughmacrory

MY BEST FRIEND

My best friend is kind
She is very friendly
She is fab
She is class
She shares all her things with me
Plays with me all the time
She never ever falls out with me
Sometimes she comes down to my house
I go down to her house too
It is very good to have
A best friend.

Grace Dobbs (9)
St Teresa's Primary School, Loughmacrory

BEST FRIEND

I have a best friend
A best friend who is very kind
A best friend who is very polite
A best friend who is very good
A best friend who is very cool
It is very good to have
A best friend.

Megan O'Brien (9)
St Teresa's Primary School, Loughmacrory

SPORT

I like all kinds of sport
Football is the best of all
Kick the ball
Run all over the place
And then you score a goal
Yes! It's in the net
I jump and dance
But soon settle down!

Liam McCartan (9)
St Teresa's Primary School, Loughmacrory

MY BEST FRIEND

My best friend is really good fun
We like to play in the sun
Running and jumping all day
My best friend is really good

We can run and climb up trees
My best friend is really good
We made a tree hut in the field
I like my best friend.

Conor Donnelly (10)
St Teresa's Primary School, Loughmacrory

STARS IN THEIR EYES

I did 'Stars In Their Eyes' with Grace and Emma,
On the fifteenth of November,
We sang and danced,
We were Atomic Kitten singing 'The Tide is High'.
A boy, Feidhlim won, he sang 'Grease Lightning'.
My dad played Matthew Kelly,
Erin and Paola helped us with the dance.

Danielle O'Donnell (8)
St Teresa's Primary School, Loughmacrory

MY MIND IN DREAM

My mind, inside,
Is like a fantasy world,
When I am sleeping,
Once I thought and thought hard,
I looked out of the window,
The next minute I was in Cuba,
Then in Spain!
Ring, ring, oh it's only a dream!

Grainne O'Goan (8)
St Teresa's Primary School, Loughmacrory

BEST TRENDS

Best trends are just like friends,
Best trends is fashion,
Best trends are cool,
Sometimes I think best trends is you!

Best trends is style,
Best trends bends
All around the world
And never stops.

Best trends like my mummy,
She buys them every day
And when I get them,
I scream and shout, 'Yeah!'

Amanda Kelly (8)
St Teresa's Primary School, Loughmacrory

POKÉMON

Pokémon are cool, Pokémon are class
Pikachu and Magnamite can do electric blasts
Staru and Starmie can do water gun
And Pidgey and Pigeot can fly over the sun

Pinsir and Torous have a big horn
And Togepi was in a shell before he was born
Mankey and Primape like to fight a lot
And in Goldenrod City, the game corner has lots of slots.

Niall McClements (9)
St Teresa's Primary School, Loughmacrory

HANDBALL

Handball is good and it is great,
You learn to play handball,
Sometimes you get to play handball matches,
Sometimes you play your sister and your friend,
Every Wednesday, Ciara and I go to handball training,
Afterwards we'll be very hot,
Our handball coaches are Patricia and Michael John.

Aisling McDermott (9)
St Teresa's Primary School, Loughmacrory

HANDBALL

'Handball is my favourite sport to play,
I like handball.'
'So I do!'
'I love handball,
I love handball.'
'So I do! So I do!'
'I like going to handball.'
'So I do!'
We all love handball.

Ciara Dobbs (8)
St Teresa's Primary School, Loughmacrory